S0-AUK-228

BASKETBALL FUN

by Tyler Omoth

raintree

a Capstone company — publishers for children

Raintree is an imprint of Capstone Global Library Limited, a company incorporated in England and Wales having its registered office at 264 Banbury Road, Oxford, OX2 7DY – Registered company number: 6695582

www.raintree.co.uk
myorders@raintree.co.uk

Edited by Shelly Lyons
Designed by Tracy McCabe
Original illustrations © Capstone Global Library Limited 2021
Picture research by Svetlana Zhurkin
Production by Laura Manthe
Originated by Capstone Global Library Ltd
Printed and bound in India

978 1 3982 0334 1 (hardback)
978 1 3982 0333 4 (paperback)

British Library Cataloguing in Publication Data
A full catalogue record for this book is available from the British Library.

Acknowledgements
We would like to thank the following for permission to reproduce photographs: Alamy: Steve Skjold, 18; iStockphoto: FatCamera, 8, 15, 16; Shutterstock: Ahturner, cover (left), dnaveh, 9, Fafarumba, cover (right), back cover, 1, glenda, 21, Monkey Business Images, 17, onuk, 13, Ory Gonian, 7, Paolo Bona, 5, 10, Patty Chan (background), back cover and throughout, pedalist, 6, Sergey Novikov, 11, 14, SpeedKingz, 19

Every effort has been made to contact copyright holders of material reproduced in this book. Any omissions will be rectified in subsequent printings if notice is given to the publisher.

All the internet addresses (URLs) given in this book were valid at the time of going to press. However, due to the dynamic nature of the internet, some addresses may have changed, or sites may have changed or ceased to exist since publication. While the author and publisher regret any inconvenience this may cause readers, no responsibility for any such changes can be accepted by either the author or the publisher.

CONTENTS

Words in **bold** are in the glossary.

WHAT IS BASKETBALL?

Basketball is a fun game. It is played between two teams. Each team has five players. Teams move a ball up and down a **court**. They score points when the ball goes through a hoop. The team that gets the most points wins.

WHAT DO I NEED TO PLAY?

The first thing you need to play basketball is a ball. Most basketballs are orange with black stripes. They are filled with air. The air helps them to bounce.

You also need a hoop, called a basket.

It hangs on a board, called a **backboard**.

You get points when the ball goes through the hoop.

You need good shoes to play basketball. Many players wear high-tops. These shoes have tall tops. The tops hold your ankles.

treads

High-tops also have rubber **treads**. The treads grip the floor. They help you move fast. They also stop you slipping.

WHERE DO I PLAY?

Basketball is played on a large, flat floor called a court. Basketball courts can be inside or outside.

Outdoor courts are often concrete,
but can be made of other materials.
Indoor courts can be made of wood.
All courts have a basket at each end.

Basketball courts have many lines. The sidelines show the edges of the court. A centre line marks the middle of the court. A 3-point line bends around each basket. **Free-throw lines** are in front of the baskets.

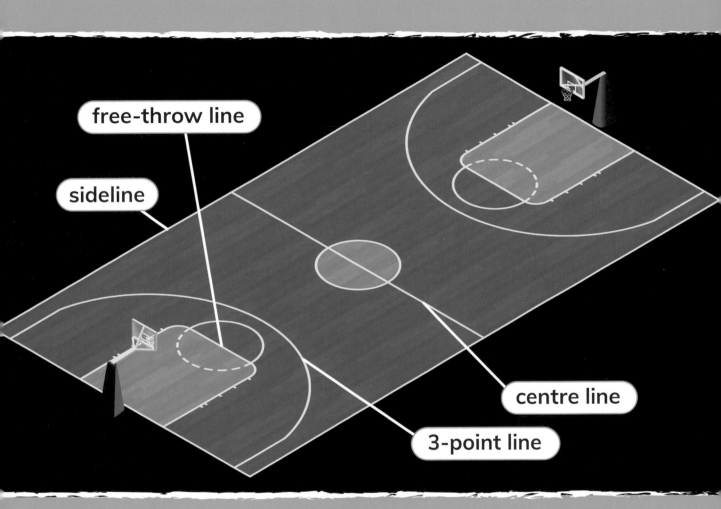

free-throw line

sideline

centre line

3-point line

13

HOW DO I PLAY?

The aim of basketball is to score points. Teams score when they get baskets. Most shots score two points. Shots from outside the 3-point line score three points.

Free throws are worth one point. Players shoot free throws when the other team **fouls** them. A foul is a move that is against the rules.

During a game, teams move the ball across the court. But players can't carry the ball. They must pass it or dribble it. Players dribble by bouncing the ball on the floor.

Basketball games last four **quarters**. After two quarters, players take a break called **half-time**. When the game ends, the team with the most points wins.

HOW CAN I BE A GOOD SPORT?

Basketball is fun when everyone plays fair. Good sports share the ball with players on their team. They let others take shots.

Good sports follow the rules and listen
to their coach. After the game, they shake
hands with the other team. They make
playing basketball fun!

SKILL BUILDER: DRIBBLING

Players dribble to move the ball up and down the basketball court. Learn to dribble with these simple steps:

1. Balance the basketball in one hand and then drop it. When the ball bounces up, use the same hand to push it back down. Be careful not to slap the ball. Just give it a gentle push.

2. Keep bouncing the ball with one hand. See how many times you can do it without stopping.

3. Once you have the hang of it, bounce the ball to your other hand. Practise dribbling with that hand. Then dribble the ball back and forth from one hand to the other.

4. When you can dribble with both hands, try walking while dribbling. Then try running!

GLOSSARY

backboard wood or plastic surface attached to a basketball hoop

court area where games are played

foul action that is against the rules, such as pushing or tripping

free-throw line line from which a free shot is taken after a foul

half-time short break in the middle of a game

quarter one of four equal periods in a basketball game

tread ridges on the sole of a shoe that keep it from slipping

FIND OUT MORE

BOOKS

Basketball (Fantastic Sport Facts), Michael Hurley (Raintree, 2013)

Children's Book of Sport, DK (DK Children, 2011)

Full Court Flash (Sports Illustrated Kids Graphic Novel), Scott Ciencin (Raintree, 2019)

WEBSITES

www.bbl.org.uk

www.dkfindout.com/uk/sports/basketball

www.sikids.com

INDEX